Lapi‹

Beginners

Step by Step Guide to Tumbling, Cutting, Faceting

(How to Find and Identify Gems Precious Minerals Geodes and Fossils Like an Advanced)

John Davis

Published By **Andrew Zen**

John Davis

Lapidary for Beginners: Step by Step Guide to Tumbling, Cutting, Faceting (How to Find and Identify Gems Precious Minerals Geodes and Fossils Like an Advanced)

ISBN   978-1-7782476-8-2

No part of this guidebook shall be reproduced in any form without permission in writing from the publisher except in the case of brief quotations embodied in critical articles or reviews.

Legal & Disclaimer

The information contained in this book is not designed to replace or take the place of any form of medicine or professional medical advice. The information in this book has been provided for educational & entertainment purposes only.

The information contained in this book has been compiled from sources deemed reliable, and it is accurate to the best of the Author's knowledge; however, the Author cannot guarantee its accuracy and validity and cannot be held liable for any errors or omissions. Changes are periodically made to this book. You must consult your doctor or get professional medical advice before using any of the suggested remedies, techniques, or information in this book.

Table Of Contents

Chapter 1: Understanding Lapidary

Let us begin with the fundamentals:

What Is Lapidary?

Lapidary is the artwork of accumulating, decreasing, shaping, and sharpening precious gem stones, minerals, and stones. Someone who does all of the above is referred to as a lapidarist. In next chapters, we will speak the specific valuable minerals and stones within the worldwide these days.

Lapidary isn't always a cutting-edge issue.

Eons within the past, a stone also can have by way of hazard flaked or broken after falling into a hearth, or likely someone had hammered a stone by means of the usage of using smacking one stone against every unique and observed out it became feasible to apply it as a device. The truth is, nobody absolutely is aware about on the equal time as lapidary started out out.

This is due to the fact this artwork dates again to prehistory at the identical time as humans started out fashioning weapons and gear from stone after expertise that some stones are greater hard than others.

Fast in advance to the Nineteen Fifties whilst this artwork have grow to be famous within the United States as a few specialists have end up famous for lowering and sharpening gemstones, then fabricating them to in form severa jewelry settings.

Is Venturing Into Lapidary Profitable?

To answer this question, allow us to take a look at some topics.

If you narrow a stone with a high-quality cloth along with garnet, tourmaline, or quartz every week and if the stones weigh from one to 6 carats, you can promote them for everywhere amongst US$a hundred fifty and US$500[3]. This amount is pretty rewarding, bearing in mind that the not unusual profits of complete-time personnel are US$1,041[4] every week.

According to the Gem society, you could make spherical US$2,500 as gross earnings every week, which means that that during a month, you will with out a trouble bag US$10,000 (that is 20 stones that weigh one to six carats)!

Comparing this to our initial amount of US$1,041 each week for popular complete-time artwork, which translates to US$4,164 each month, lapidary is a rewarding project, don't you compromise?

Let us circulate deeper.

For instance, if you challenge into faceting on my own, allow us to have a look at how an entire lot you could earn. Let us say you purchase a hard piece of sunstone for round US$10 steady with carat, k? That approach you could pay US$one hundred if you buy 10 carats, right?

With this in mind, you may sell this difficult piece of gemstone for US$one hundred in keeping with carat after cutting it, especially as it will weigh spherical three.Five carats. You may have earned a entire of US$350 on the prevent – now not horrible, right?

Chapter 2: Understanding More About Gems And Stones

There are 4 maximum important gemstones:

Diamonds

Diamond is famous because the hardest treasured stone acknowledged due to its herbal carbon composition. We generally weigh diamonds in carats, in which 1 carat equals two hundred milligrams.

You are in all likelihood curious approximately wherein we discover diamonds. Well, they will be normally positioned in 3 vital styles of deposits. These are:

- Alluvial gravels: These gravels embody free silt, sand, clay, or gravel deposited on circulate beds.

- Glacial tills: These tills encompass tiny particles and large boulders, all combined up.

- Kimberlite pipes: Kimberlite is placed deep into the earth's thrust, frequently among 100 and 300km under the crust.

Sapphires

Sapphire is a gemstone from a mineral called corundum, a crystallized form of aluminum oxide. You will choose out out sapphires with out problem because of the reality they have got a very specific blue shade but furthermore are to be had in white, crimson, crimson, yellow, and green sun shades, amongst others.

We degree sapphire in millimeters and discover them in deposits in countries including Vietnam, Montana, Thailand, Tanzania, Sri Lanka, Nigeria, Myanmar, Mozambique, Malawi, Madagascar, Laos,

Kenya, India, Ethiopia, Colombia, Shandong China, Cameroon, Cambodia, Afghanistan, and Australia.

Emeralds

Emerald is from a mineral called beryl and is understood for its charming inexperienced colour. Beryl, its mineral, consists of additives which consist of vanadium and chromium that offers the gemstone its inexperienced colour.

Like many gems, we use carats to weigh emeralds. Emeralds fee amongst US$1 steady with carat to spherical US$one hundred,000 steady with carat. Emeralds are typically mined in international locations together with Colombia, Zambia, and Brazil

Rubies

Rubies are pinkish-red to blood-red gem stones fashioned from a mineral called corundum. Like most one in every of a type gem stones, we weigh rubies in carats. You will in widespread find out them in mines which encompass Burma—which has the excellent rubies within the worldwide—Vietnam, Sri Lanka, Pakistan, Mozambique, Malawi, Madagascar, India, Cambodia, Australia, and Afghanistan, among others.

These four valuable stones are called the easy ones. The following are semi-treasured stones:

Alexandrite

Alexandrite, which comes from a mineral referred to as chrysoberyl, is a semi-valuable stone because of the truth it is instead each emerald and ruby. Under daylight hours, it has a inexperienced colour however turns red in incandescent mild. Alexandrite is arguably one of the maximum costly gems because of the reality its fee can pass up as high as US$15,000 in keeping with carat[6]!

Alexandrite have become at the start determined in Russia's Ural Mountains within the 1830s however is now commonplace in worldwide places collectively with Sri Lanka, Brazil, and East Africa.

Zircon

Zircon is a gemstone together with components which includes zirconium and zirconium silicate, giving it its inexperienced, dark brown, or crimson colour after extraction, with the color changing on the equal time as you warmth it. Depending on zircon's coloration intensity, length, and readability, outstanding zircons that weigh over 10 carats will supply in between US$3 hundred and US$400 in step with carat[7]!

The first-rate component approximately zircon is that it does not have herbal specific mining places. That is due to the reality it's miles aplenty in metamorphic rocks or igneous rocks. However, it is not uncommon in Australia, Florida, India, and Brazil.

Turquoise

Turquoise is an opaque mineral with a blue-to-inexperienced colour fashioned from copper and aluminum phosphates. It is an extremely good gem because it isn't clean to find out, and there are not such a lot of inside the international.

For years, North America changed into the number one mining spot for this gem, but it's miles typically located in

Nevada, Arizona, and in a few cases, California.

Tourmaline

Tourmaline is a completely black or blackish mineral from prismatic crystals (crystals that display a uniform bypass-phase) determined in granite and special styles of rocks.

You will sell tourmaline steady with its variety and its incredible. However, the maximum pricey tourmalines are Paraiba because they price spherical US$1,000 consistent with carat[8]! Tourmalines are aplenty in Namibia, Malawi, Kenya, Mozambique, Madagascar, Nigeria, Tanzania, and greater frequently than now not in Brazil

Tanzanite

Tanzanite is a precious stone that comes from a mineral called zoisite. This stone is unique because it has a totally unique violet/blue color. If you get it in its tough shape, this stone will radiate 3 maximum essential hues: red, violet, and blue.

As the decision suggests, Tanzanites normally come from the northern a part of Tanzania. Although it expenses lower than diamonds, the price constant with carat will variety among US$3 hundred and US$600.[9]

Spinel

Spinel is classified as an extended lasting gemstone; it levels in color from orange to excessive crimson or purple. It additionally is available in blue, purple, bluish-green, or violet colorations. We can not study spinels to sapphires, diamonds, or rubies, but if you art work on spinels with the right awesome, you will have no hassle getting any amount among US$1,000 and US$7,000![10]

Spinels are placed in the gravel beds of Sri Lanka, Madagascar, and Tanzania, the marble deposits of Vietnam, and in special international locations which include Kenya, Brazil, and northern Asia.

Peridot

Peridot is a semi-treasured, conventional August birthstone composed of silicon dioxide decided in a mineral called olivine. It typically forms in lava flows anywhere inside the worldwide. However, global locations including the united states, Vietnam, Tanzania, Pakistan, China, and Myanmar are famous for having healthy portions in their deposits.

You can get shimmering green glowing peridots in Hawaii because the place is whole of historical lava due to volcanic eruptions. According to severa assets, peridot sells for US$50 to US$80 to around US$450 for first-class specimens[11]!

Pearl

Pearls are pretty particular gem stones. Most of the gem stones and stones we've were given said to this point come from the ground, right? Well, pearls come from residing creatures called mussels and oysters.

If you need pearls from freshwater ponds and rivers, look for regions complete of mussels. On the opportunity hand, in case you want if pearls from salt water, search for them in regions frequented via oysters.

You will discover pearls in China, off the coast of Japan, Polynesia, France, and Australia. The expenses variety from round US$one hundred< to tens of masses of lots of greenbacks[12]!

Moonstone

Moonstone is a gemstone made from minerals: albite and orthoclase. That is why you'll see this stone having stacked layers.

The fantastic first-class moonstone comes from Southern India and Sri Lanka, and unique moonstone versions come from the usa, Brazil, Mexico, Armenia, and Australia. Moonstones are averagely precious because of the reality if you make the exquisite tremendous, you may get around US$250[13].

Opal

Opal is a semi-precious stone from the silica mineral own family, which has a shimmering milky, iridescence appearance commonly utilized in earrings. As of these days, styles of opals collectively with gem black, crystal, boulder, and white opals are considered the most high-priced, and opals are one of the worldwide's most treasured gemstones! For instance, wonderful black opal fees over US$10,000 in line with carat.[14]

You will locate opal anywhere inside the worldwide. But mainly, you may find out it inside the Western factors of america, Honduras, Mexico, and Brazil.

Garnet

Garnet moreover pass via the red gem or the January Birthstone; they arrive from silicon-containing minerals. This gem isn't always new due to the reality humankind has used it because the Bronze Age as adorns, earrings, and abrasives.

In most instances, garnet comes inside the colorings purple, green, yellow, orange, and red. Different assets document that garnets promote from US$500 everyday with carat to round US$7,000 in line with carat for excellent garnet stones[15].

Aquamarine

Aquamarine is an great blue-inexperienced birthstone from the beryl family and includes a silicon element known as beryllium aluminum silicate.

You will discover it in numerous international places, together with Mozambique, Pakistan, Zambia, Madagascar, Nigeria, and Brazil. As for rate, if you cognizance on darkish blue to slightly greenish blue aquamarine gems, you could fetch round US$1,000 consistent with carat.[16]

Amethyst

Also referred to as "the all-reason stone," amethyst is a member of the quartz family. It is obvious, coarse-grained, and regarded as a shielding stone.

You will find out this gem in countries which includes South India, the US, Russia, South Korea, Uruguay, and broadly speakme in Brazil. As for charge, amethyst isn't always so expensive, especially because of the truth round eighty percentage of it floats around and is artificial. So, you'll locate that the rate degrees from US$20 up to US$50 in keeping with carat[17].

We can pass on and on, listing the wonderful semi-valuable stones said to man, but the ones we have were given stated to date are the maximum not unusual.

With this number one statistics on valuable stones and gems, allow us to skip on and awareness on walking on our stones and gems via using first getting to know about the lapidary tools you could want:

Chapter 3: Basic Lapidary Tools

As a lapidary novice, the following are the gear of the change you may need:

The rock hammer

This hammer is good for decreasing large rocks to small quantities. Many will let you recognize that a determined will work for the same purpose, but the fact is that a few blows from the rock hammer will paintings higher. Therefore, I urge you operate a rock hammer due to the reality it's miles greater accurate than different strategies, especially whilst dealing with fractured stones and gems.

Only use the rock hammer for cabbing raw materials with minimum to mild charge. DO NOT use a rock hammer on luxurious pieces of difficult stones and gemstones due to the truth you can lose a large part of the stone, which can be very pricey, important to losses in area of profits.

Also, NEVER use this sort of hammer on precious stones which includes calcite or opal due to the fact you can reduce the shape of useable areas as this may reduce the precious stone's price. For such substances, use saws and tile nippers.

Saws

As cited, saws are ideal for reducing fragile gems like uvarovite, opal, hessonite, and lazulite, amongst others.

There are particular styles of observed blades. They embody:

- Circular found blades – These are all-purposed

- Steel spherical observed blades – These are remarkable for clean materials

- High-tempo steel round observed blades – These are top notch for tough substances

- Carbide spherical noticed blades – These are first-rate for hard substances

- Abrasive saw blades – These are all-purposed

- Diamond wire blades – These are current device that paintings better than all the considered one of a kind sorts of blades

Tile Nippers

Tile nippers is probably immensely useful even as eliminating small quantities of materials from your thing hard edges. Using them is likewise clean because of the truth you notable want to vicinity the nippers inside the wonderful location and squeeze. You will word that in evaluation to using a noticed for the equal motive, nippers are more correct.

You also can use nippers at the same time as coping with fractures. You will fine need to press at the fracture, to have the potential to help you finish splitting the cloth, and from this, you can shop extra fabric than sawing, no matter how cautious you want to be.

Grinders

Many will urge you to apply a observed for slicing difficult stones. The fact, however, is that a grinder will assist you do the same however with extra manage. However, while using a grinder, be cautious because of the reality if you use it on a sensitive material, you threat it shattering, if you want to be a loss to your end.

Dremel

A Dremel is one of the maximum bendy gadget as it will help you cut hard stone materials, then sand, buff, and polish gem stones.

Chisel

A chisel is one of the quality gear to have to your toolbox because it will assist you narrow rocks. All you need to do is be careful — mind-set your hammer and chisel, then hammer the chisel down with the rock held firmly in place.

Ensure you use a chisel fabricated from iron due to the reality they ultimate longer and offer the desired consequences.

Faceting Machine

If your reason is accuracy and comfortability, purchase a gem faceting device. However, earlier than looking for this device, choose out the traits you need. For instance, if you want a faceting device that offers repeatability, this means that you desire a device that produces the equal impact each time you cut a stone, then circulate for a device that does not need reinvention.

If you want a dependable faceting device, get a gadget that desires little renovation and in case you are seeking out a brief-faceting gadget, get one that is less complicated to apply, due to this it will in shape your velocity, consequently supporting you produce greater inner a brief time

With those few issues in mind, permit us to take a look at the unique varieties of machines;

1: The Hand Piece Faceting Machine

This faceting gadget is greater correct than a device which embody a jam peg machine. It is quicker and further adaptable as you can absolutely circulate the handpiece spherical, making it tons much less tough to get your chosen view on the equal time as running on your valuable stone and gem.

This tool also makes it less hard to take the stone out and placed it yet again into the handpiece than taking a stone from a cutter to a separate polisher.

2: The Jam Peg Faceting Machine

As you can in all likelihood tell from the picture above, this type of faceting machine is 'antique university.' However, being traditional has benefits because of the reality this faceting device is outstanding for manufacturing!

The downside to this machine is that it isn't so correct for a few because it's far based upon on the approach used. In addition to not being as accurate as some of the opposite faceting machines on this list, the device has an extended studying curve.

three: The Mast Faceting Machine

This sort of faceting tool is considered one of the maximum accurate. Thus, that is the system you ought to get if you are in a aggressive surroundings and need to supply specific satisfactory merchandise.

The mast faceting machines are smooth to study as compared to at least one-of-a-type faceting machines. However, they're truly wrong for speed reducing.

So, how does a faceting device paintings?

Let us take an instance:

If you're to reduce a Brazilian amethyst, those are the easy steps you may take;

I will facet this stone the usage of the Portuguese style —we're in a function to discuss this in next chapters. All you need to recognize to date is this fashion helps maximize the stone's colour, making it seem deeper colored but extremely good.

Before faceting it, this stone weighed a hint over ninety one carats

I will start the faceting manner with the resource of supergluing a brass pinnacle to the difficult gemstone.

Next, I will location the brass into the coil of the faceting system.

After setting the right grinder into the gadget and making use of some lubricant, I will start faceting the stone.

Kindly word that there are a few extra topics we need to do on the same time as running with a device, but this must come up with a difficult concept of the manner this system normally works.

A faceting device has the subsequent components:

- Laps – this allows in lowering and sharpening the stone

You will need different sorts. For instance, you'll want one for:

- Roughing the stone

- Cutting the stone

- Fine decreasing the stone

- Abrasives – These will assist polish the gem or stone.

- A dopping station – This detail will help you placed the stone onto the device.

- A dop holder – This will help you be part of the stone.

- Wax and oil lamp – The oil lamp will assist you to effectively soften the wax you could use with the dop holder.

- Transfer jig – This will assist you switch a stone or a gem from one aspect to the opportunity.

Magnifier

Better referred to as a loupe, this tool will assist you have got a look at the stone or gem for fracture, coloration, and inclusions.

Acetone

Acetone will help you dispose of any stains for your gems or stones.

Light

This may be sincere, but you need to get the fantastic light that offers you the maximum practical view. Get an synthetic white mild or daylight hours mild as it has a color temperature of around 5000K and 5500K.

Marker

Sharpies will are available in to be had for marking regions to lessen or label.

Rock Tumbling Grit

This artificial silicon abrasive will help you get via hard particles. In exceptional terms, a rock tumbling grit is a substance that will help you do grinding with out troubles

Plastic Pellets

These pellets will act as a filler on the same time as tumbling rocks. Also, pellets are great for sensitive rocks because of the fact the ones rocks without difficulty overwhelm or destroy —bear in mind, we want to shop as loads stone or gem as possible.

With our equipment organized, we want to bear in mind some safety precautions before we get to the lapidary device.

Let us talk this subsequent.

Chapter 4: Lapidary Safety Precautions

The maximum crucial protection precautions to adhere to within the direction of the lapidary manner encompass:

Get Rid of The Dust

Since we are able to be doing loads of grinding, the possibilities of you either breathing in or consuming stone and gem dirt is immoderate. For a few, such dirt also can purpose allergies and illnesses which incorporates dermatitis.

To address this trouble, make sure your walking place has proper air flow. You can opt for unique styles of air flow, consisting of:

- Local air flow – This involves taking the damaging components produced away from your operating area by means of sucking.

- Dilution air waft – Here, you open the window right subsequent to you, because of this permitting air to bypass on its manner out

To put off dirt, I suggest the use of a fume hood.

All you need to do is to area this close to the lower lower back of your workshop. It will make sure a loose go with the flow of air while exits are blocked. However, check that your fume hood works thru developing synthetic smoke before on foot.

Always Wear Protective Gear

Before running on any lapidary method, have the following;

Apron

Safety glasses

Filtration Mask

Rubber/Plastic Gloves

Eye Rinse

Ear protection

In addition to sporting shielding gear for safety in the route of subjects together with dust, you need to endure in thoughts some matters;

- Always move for reducing oils loose from components including amines or nitrates. Oils containing the ones additives are unstable to apply as they'll purpose ailments which include most cancers[18]. In addition, amines may additionally reason[19] complications, breathing problems, hypersensitive reactions, and excessive blood pressure.

- If your garb is infected on the identical time as working with oils, I recommend changing proper now, especially when you have been no longer sporting any aprons. If the oils touch any exposed regions of your pores and skin, wash those elements with cleaning soap and water. In addition, bathe frequently and comply with creams with non-amine boundaries for brought protection.

Always Use Efficient Materials

As I turn out to be demonstrating how a faceting device works, do you hold in mind us discussing a few thing about lubricants? Well, a few lapidarist use water in preference to oils. The key component here is to use the proper substances, ALWAYS! Also, use substances which might be of right excellent that will help you keep away from injuries and the production of lousy superb gemstones and stones

So, with water, for example, avoid getting the water anywhere in the jogging desk and the overall walking place, and ensure that the hose you use drains water well. To do that, constantly take a look at if your hose works nicely each time earlier than you begin running.

With your device equipped, it is time you get proper to industrial company. "How," you may ask? By getting to know what goes on within the route of lapidary.

Let us communicate this next.

Chapter 5: The Lapidary Process

The lapidary approach starts with getting the extraordinary first-class hard. Since we're able to not be going to mines in certainly one of a kind factors of the u . S . A ., you'll contact distinct difficult dealers. When you eventually get your tough provider, the subsequent step may be to evaluate the tough to get the great pleasant available.

Now the query is, "How will you get the terrific great?" Let us answer this next.

How Do I Get The Best Quality Of Rough?

When trying to find difficult, keep in mind what I call the Two C Classifications. These are;

1: Clarity

Always attention at the extent of transparency of the gemstone (transparency right right right here manner how a whole lot mild a given gem or stone transmits light). The more transparent a stone or a gem is, the higher its charge can be.

So right here are a few tips at the way to understand if a gemstone tough is actual;

- Test the stone to discover if it is artificial or herbal: There is a thin line amongst natural and artificial. To differentiate some of the 2, do the following;

- Check for any inclusion: Use a magnifier in case you cannot see any inclusions together with your bare eyes. In addition to looking for inclusions, look for marks, cracks, black spots, or chippings. With all this in thoughts, diamonds which have few inclusions are higher. As for colored gems, study that inclusions are not awful too —in most instances— however may additionally moreover every so often be complicated, depending on your patron. The bottom line is that inclusions show that the stated gem or stone is actual and not artificial.

- In addition to the use of a magnifier to test if the gem has inclusions, you may rub the uncut stone or gem across a ceramic tile or each different unglazed cloth. Doing this need to go away some powder, higher called a streak, that have to be the same colour because the gemstone.

You can also use a gem tester.

This tester uses thermal or electric conduction to check the quantity of heat or electricity tempo this is going thru the stone.

2: Carat

After readability, consider the carat — described due to the fact the degree of the fitness of gold. You can think about it due to the fact the ratio of 24-karat gold to the alloy metals in a particular combination.[20]

By citing carat, I urge you to maintain in mind the load and duration of the tough and the finished gemstone.

Fundamentally, one carat equals 1/5th of a gram. You can also say that one carat equals two hundred milligrams. You may hear others using the phrase "factor," which is not hard to apprehend. The critical detail to apprehend is that one carat equals 100 factors.

Therefore, the primary aspect to do is thoughts your hard's weight. But at the same time as you consider that you'll be handling difficult, you need to be smart at estimating how a exquisite deal weight to take away in exceptional situations.

Let us speak this subsequent.

First, allow us to say you have were given were given a hard that has a fracture, proper? For this one, you could need to estimate how a whole lot that removed particles or vicinity will weigh because it can have an effect at the burden of the completed stone or gem.

The simple issue to phrase is that the extra gently long-set up the tough is, the better the weight and period yield. On the opportunity hand, if you'll be strolling with a tough that has plenty of projections, assume a decrease yield in phrases of weight and period.

Another critical trouble to recall in advance than working for your difficult is what weight you want to have on the end. The Gem Society[21] says you can assume to hold a 33 percentage weight after running from a massive bite of

42

difficult. However, if you are reducing stone in keeping with unique settings or calibrations, expect a smaller size and weight yield.

For instance, permit's say you could artwork on a hard to be able to give you an oval gemstone sized 9x5mm; this can probably weigh 2 carats or barely tons much less.

On the opposite hand, if the client wants an oval length 7x5mm, the yield will lower to a chunk weighing round 1 carat. I, therefore, recommend that you ALWAYS keep this in thoughts while handling hard.

With our hard prepared, permit us to pass earlier and go through unique lapidary strategies so that it will lead us to finish stones and gems;

Step 1: Getting the Rough

After getting our real rough, the following step is to decide how you want your tough given to you. For example, lots less uncommon gems and stones are normally reduce as calibrations. Calibrations are commonplace because, in the ones sizes, you could with out troubles reduce the hard in a single-of-a-type custom sizes without paying too much interest to the mounting, a chunk of metallic that holds a gem inner a bit of jewelry.

For instance, if you seek out first-rate, uncommon tough, you will use this to dictate your forestall piece because of the reality you will want to maximise the entire stone or gem —you may not need to lose some thing due to the reality, for such stones and gem stones, more weight equals extra money.

Step 2: Planning How to Cut the Rough

With your tough in hand and with it being the size you want, the next step may be to bear in mind a manner to reduce the hard.

One of the maximum important subjects to do not forget is what tool you could use. The vital rule is to reduce the tough the usage of a tougher fabric than the rock.

The National Park Service[22] gives us a breakdown of which tool to use on the identical time as jogging with unique stones and gemstones. Please phrase that the list is not entire as the listing of stones and gemstones is pretty substantial, but it lays the foundation.

When it entails hammers, hold in thoughts what stone you may artwork on; as an instance:

The pointed-tip rock hammer can be useful while handling difficult roughs together with granite. Its square aspect will assist in cracking open the rock, while its pointed prevent will assist in scraping out some samples if required.

The crack hammer is useful in cracking, splitting, and breaking rocks. Through the impact of this hammer, you will be able to repair in chisels and pry backs into the cracks

When you in the long run get to the softer debris so that you can get entry to your tough, you may need to exchange the hammer to a chisel-edged rock hammer. The chiseled give up will make splitting the tough's layers much less complex.

Once you test the tools off the listing, consider the stone you'll be walking on. If it has any inclusions, as an instance, don't forget how you may cast off them. In addition, reflect onconsideration on zoning. Ask your self questions at the side of;

- How do you want the gemstone considered from the table?

- How do you need to orient the gemstone to ensure its bands run parallel with the desk facet?

Fundamentally:

Knowing the way to lessen the stone in advance than you begin doing it will decide how the rest of the lapidary manner will skip.

Different Gemstone Forms to Consider

You would probably marvel, "What shapes or forms must you preserve in mind in advance than I start operating on it?"

Cabochons

Look on the photo above. What are you capable of phrase? You can likely phrase the dome form and a backside that looks flat. All this is referred to as a cabochon. If making a decision to go together with this form, you will not want to thing it.

That way we're able to form the tough to be able to have a flat top, several polished faces, and a pointed bottom — we are capable of expound in this in subsequent chapters. All you can want to do is polish it.

Why are some stones or gemstones cabochon reduce?

Those who select this shape accomplish that as it works nicely with stones or gemstones with too many imperfections or translucent to be shaped in another way, together with faceting (we will talk this in element in subsequent chapters).

What stones or gemstones ought to take this form?

Well:

This shape works for specific businesses of stones, which encompass:

- Chatoyant: Stones and gemstones that have meditated slight that actions underneath the stone's or gem's surface)

- Opalescent: These are obvious or translucent-searching stones),

- Iridescent: These are stones or gemstones that display their colors top notch whilst white mild displays within the route of them)

- Asteriated: These are stones or gem stones that have a celebrity form when you take a look at them), and

- Opaque: These stones do no longer permit any slight to bypass via.

Sculptures

Many would possibly probably suppose that rings is the best detail we can style from gems. The reality is that you may additionally carve them into sculptures and figurines. One vital element to be aware with carving gem stones is that it works awesome while the usage of semi-precious stones.

Why carve gems?

Sometimes, you could have some leftovers after walking on a difficult stone. In such instances, in choice to questioning what to do with that fabric, turn them into great gem stones that add for your yield. You can also decide to in maximum instances take a huge piece of difficult and flip it right right into a big specific masterpiece! Think about what works for you!

What semi-valuable stones and gemstones are best for sculptures?

These embody carnelian, serpentinite, jasper, onyx, agate, clean quartz, and jade.

Cameos and Intaglios

If you need a specific photo on pinnacle of the precept material, glide for the Cameos and Intaglios shapes. Specifically, with intaglio, you can carve or engrave an picture into the gemstones and go away the facts hole. On the opportunity hand, with cameos, you can make a shape with specific coloured layers: one layer can also additionally have a raised historic beyond, and the alternative can have figures carved.

What stones and gems are quality for Cameos and Intaglios?

Some gemstones and stones perfect for making this shape embody sardonyx, onyx, agate, obsidian, lapis lazuli, jasper, garnet, cornelian, chalcedony, and amethyst.

Inlays

Creating an inlay approach you could layout a form that you could be part of with a few thing else. From the image above, you may see the gem ready into a ring. That is much like what you may do whilst developing inlays. Inlays are pinnacle with jewelry, but you may custom-make one which fits into timber, steel, and distinctive stone office work.

What are the satisfactory stones and gem stones for inlays?

The outstanding stones and gemstones you can purchase as hard for inlays are opal, malachite, turquoise, onyx, and lapis lazuli, amongst others.

Spheres and beads

As the call shows, you can decide to lessen your gem and stone into beads and spheres. The excellent manner to attain this shape is to use semi-treasured stones and gems collectively with emerald, ruby, and sapphire, among others.

Faceted Stones

These stone kinds are reduce just so the stone gets a flat top and numerous polished faces —referred to as aspects— and a pointed backside.

If you or your customer desires a gem or a stone that sends the slight inwards and suggests mild at the outside thru the sides (the aspects in this case), this is the form you have to take into account.

After considering the manner to lessen the difficult stone, the subsequent step is considering what format or approach you'll use on that stone or gem.

Let us communicate this next.

Different Cutting Techniques to Consider

Here are the unique stone-decreasing strategies you need to bear in mind:

Sawing

At one factor or the opportunity, you could likely use this approach with all of your stone and gem tasks. Sawing includes the usage of a skinny spherical blade that time and again rotates as its scratches its manner through the gemstone.

However, you'll no longer use this blade by myself. You will need some liquid, together with water, to wash away the debris on the same time as on the identical time maintaining the sawblade from overheating.

Grinding

After lowering the stone or gem in line with your specs, you'll want to grind the stone or gem —in the end. Silicon carbide or diamond-impregnated wheels will are to be had available to get that stone into your chosen shape.

This technique is commonplace in pre-forming —this technique includes shaping the difficult. Once carried out shaping it into your selected form, you can visit each unique step or repeat the shaping, but with finer gadget so that it will let you obtain that very last preferred form.

Just as we used water and oil in sawing, you can use every of them to take away particles whilst additionally making sure the blades do no longer overheat.

Sanding

Grinding allows get rid of debris and form the stone higher, but sanding will produce a finer end result. While grinding, the grinder might probable have left a few scratches proper here and there; to cast off them and make it all smooth, you can want to perform a little sanding.

Lapping

Lapping may be very just like sanding and grinding. The primary distinction is that lapping might require you to carry out it to as a minimum one aspect of a lap (a rotating or a vibrating flat disk). This may be helpful while faceting because it will help you create greater-flat surfaces.

Polishing

After sawing and grounding your stone in your preferred shape and sanding it well enough to remove any difficult marks left by way of manner of manner of the grits, polish it just so it gets a mirror give up that virtually and uniquely presentations moderate. The essence of sprucing your stones is to wear out your stone's outer layer.

To polish your gems, use aluminum, chromium, tin, and cerium oxide.

For instance, under is a mixture of a polishing agent: cerium oxide.

Dip a polisher within the agent, then rub it within the path of the stone or gem.

Drilling

There will be instances in which you want to make a few component like a pendant. In such times, you can drill a hollow via your already-polished stone or gem.

To drill holes without unfavourable the stone or gem, use a rotating tube/rod with a diamond tip, a silicon carbide slurry, and coolant, or an ultrasonic/vibrating drill.

Tumbling

What when you have tiny, spherical, and immoderate gloss polished rock and mineral stones and would love to clean and refine them, however you haven't any concept the manner to move approximately it?

In that case, tumbling is for you!

Tumbling includes putting the polished gems and stones in a rock tumbler after which soaking them for in line with week or until their angles grow to be sensitive and easy! In addition to refining and cleansing them, this approach will 'heal' (make your stones stronger on the same time as simultaneously ensuring shade retention and their colourful residences do no longer get affected).

Tumbling your polished stones will not be tough. In next chapters, we can skip deeper into this manner, however in summary, all you will want to do is;

- First, have your tumbler take a seat down on a constant diploma and in an area wherein the noise of moving rocks will not trouble you and those round you.

- Next, fill the tumbler regular with its commands — approximately -thirds complete with a aggregate of water and coarse grind. Then positioned the stones interior and run the tumbler for approximately seven days until the rocks end up as clean as you need them.

- Next, do a pre-polish and a completely final polish

- Finally, wash the stones.

By this juncture inside the e book, you can have an incredible idea of the way your lapidary technique will circulate.

That way we are able to flow into without delay to the subsequent step:

Step three: Faceting

In previous sections, we went via what faceting includes in passing. This phase is going deeper into this subject count number.

The faceting method consists of reducing and sharpening gem stones and stones to a shape with a flat top, polished factors referred to as components, and a pointed bottom.

Faceting is an paintings. Faceted stones and gem stones must send moderate inwards and reflect mild at the outside thru the perimeters. The exceptional manner to accumulate that is to create a specific form: A shape with a flat top, numerous polished faces referred to as factors, and a pointed backside.

Creating this shape may be the reason of the manner explained beneath:

To start us off, permit us to get our faceting device equipped;

Faceting Tools

- A faceting system that has the following additives;

- Transfer furniture

- A forty five-degree desk block

- Index gears — we're capable of want 96, 80, or a hundred and twenty index gears

- Dops — we're able to want cones, V-dops, and residences

- Dop wax. For organisation faceted gem stones, I propose you operate immoderate-temperature brown or purple wax

- Alcohol lamp with an adjustable wick. For the alcohol lamp, we are able to use denatured alcohol

- Blazer torch

- Tweezers

- Dial caliper calibrated in millimeters

- 10X loupe

To understand greater about faceting, we want to first study its form.

What Makes Up The Facet?

From the picture above, your faceted stone need to have the subsequent components;

- Girdle: This is the widest a part of the stone; it's miles crucial to lessen and form it proper because it will set it.

- Crown: This is the pinnacle a part of the stone or gem and is placed proper on top of the girdle —because of this the choice the 'face' of the gem or stone.

- Pavilion: This is the diagonal thing of the stone or gem.

- Culet: This is the pointed backside a part of the stone or gem. The culet is in which the pavilion mains meet.

Different Faceted Shapes and Cuts

Some not unusual faceting shapes and cuts are

Kite element

Table component

Star element

Upper-half side

Not all faceted gemstones and stones have the form above. Other shapes encompass:

The Asscher

The Marquise

The Pear

The princess reduce

The radiant reduce

Knowing what shapes a faceted stone can deliver isn't enough. We should furthermore recognize which gems are brilliant for faceting. Doing this calls for that we look for one important function: tough roughs.

To degree the hardness of a gemstone, you will want to consult the Mohs Hardness Scale[23]. In one among a kind phrases, ask your hard dealer how tough the stone is. If it's miles immoderate, it's far hard and need to have a better quantity than 6.

Best Gemstones For Faceting

The super gemstones for faceting include:

Amethyst

Apatite

Citrine

Cubic Zirconia

Diopside

Emerald

Garnet

Lolite

Labradorite

Marcasite

Onyx

Peridot

Quartz

Ruby

Sapphire

Sunstone

Topaz

Tourmaline

Now that you are prepared at the side of your difficult that is right for faceting, the subsequent step will be to begin reducing the stone. Let us learn how to try this the usage of a venture. I agree with that this could be the very great manner on the way to recognize first-hand what will be required and the manner to move approximately it:

Faceting Project 1: Quartz

Materials Required

- Quartz wax

- Candle

- High-temperature wax

- Faceting tool

- 10X loupe

- A crayon of cerium oxide

- Acid

Procedure

First, placed in your shielding gadget.

Next, discover which stone you may be walking on; we're capable of paintings on quartz on this challenge.

Next, take a look at the stone or gem. Ensure it has no veil or cracks.

Next, take a towel and smooth your palms, the stone, and the metal top you may connect with the stone.

Next, warmth your wax. This assignment makes use of immoderate-temperature wax.

Next, allow the wax to kick back for 10 mins.

Next, take a look at the energy of the bond. To do that, pull the stone. Be eager no longer to drag too difficult.

Next, grind the stone's edges to your required shape. To try this, set the stone in a quill set at ninety degrees, and positioned it on a 280 grit.

To understand which grit to use for exceptional stones, examine the table underneath;

Kindly study that the higher the grit, the finer the stone may be

Grit (American Standard) dimensions

a hundred

one hundred sixty

225

240

285

325

500

600

800

1,050

1,2 hundred

2,800

four,500

five,000

8,000

9,000

thirteen,000

14,000

60,000

100,000

Given this chart, which grit is first-class for what diploma of stone lowering?

Let us take a look at this subsequent.

- Grit length among 30 and 50: These grit sizes are nice for heavy grinding. It will remove any deep scratches on the stone or gem. After using this grit duration, the stone's surface can be hard, and the scratches may be with out issues seen.

- Grit period amongst a hundred and hundred: This variety is nice for putting off deep scratches or any deeply-grooved harm on the stone. After the usage of this grit, the stone's floor may be smoother to touch. However, it's far critical to take a look at that this grit will go away the stone difficult to a point – basically, we bear in mind the moist gem anti-slip.

- Grit length among four hundred and 800: This grit period is tremendous at the same time as starting the sharpening manner. It will eliminate light scratches, giving the stone a stupid to satin shine.

- Grit length amongst 1,500 and three,000: This grit is good for the final degrees of the polishing gadget. The stop end result will cast off any harm to the stone on the equal time as furthermore generating the stone's shine.

- eight,500 and above: This grit will help supply the stone or gem a whole polish.

With this short dialogue at the brilliant styles of grits and which is awesome for which degree, permit us to move yet again to our quartz.

Next, lay the stone in opposition to the lap and lightly circulate it from side to side. This may also additionally have the high factors of the stone at the lap, making grinding viable.

As you grind, make certain you have got the appropriate duration based totally absolutely at the authentic measurements.

Next, installation your faceting device's wireless lousy boy to the right attitude: levels, then keep grinding. That will assist you carve out the pavilion. Change the lap from a 280-grit lap to a 1,two hundred-grit lap

As you preserve grinding, take the 10X loupe and determine your work to date.

Next, exchange the mindset from 40 to 44 degrees, smooth the stone with a towel, and then keep grinding. Remember, we are despite the fact that strolling at the pavilion.

Next, we can polish the stone using a lucite lap and a cerium oxide crayon. Be keener on the identical time as sprucing the stone – constantly use your 10X loupe to assess the development.

Finally, take a 45-degree adaptor, repair it, change the grit to a higher one, and complete the stone's final sprucing ranges.

What in case you do no longer have a faceting machine, is lowering and sharpening stones and gems though feasible? Well, the answer is yes! Let us do one together, we ought to?

Faceting assignment 2: Polishing Stones with a Dremel and Acid

Materials required

- A moist tile observed

Procedure

First, located to your shielding gadget.

Next, take a moist tile noticed to pores and pores and pores and skin the rock.

NOTE: Before beginning, take a 2nd to check your water tiers and verify that they're whole. We do not want the noticed to overheat.

Next, round out the edges handiest a chunk bit.

Next, smoothen the rock using a Dremel flex shaft. Mine has an easy-launch diamond blade.

Next, activate the water drip machine and make circles over the entire rock.

Next, dip the stone in acid blended with rest room cleanser to attain a deeper polish — I used Lysol rest room bowl cleaner.

Once you place the rock in, be eager to preserve an eye fixed regular on it due to the fact the acid/toilet mixture is relatively reactive. Leave the combination for a few minutes, then pour it.

Next, dip the stone in a heat water and lavatory bowl cleaner mixture. Let the stone relaxation inside the stated aggregate for 5 minutes.

Finally, rinse it off, and you're achieved.

Faceting Project three: Amethyst

This assignment cuts the stone into 1000000000000 layout; underneath is an image that suggests what a trillion-reduce layout looks as if;

Materials Required

- Faceting device

- Acetone

- Laps

Procedure

First, join the stone to the brass dipstick. To have the stone related, use any faceting wax.

Next, place your lap —choose the proper grit consistent with the listing given in advance— and begin grinding. This project starts with 260 grit and then advances to six hundred grit.

Remember to apply your loupe to evaluate the faces and a towel to disregard the debris as you keep grinding.

Next, trade the calibrations and angle to ninety-diploma, then preserve decreasing the stone.

For a finer reduce, change to a copper lap that has a grit of 8,000.

For the very last polish degree, use a dark difficulty lap with cerium oxide.

Next, bypass again for your 260 grit and use it to reduce the stone's crown.

To polish the stone, use a zirconium oxide lap. To lessen to the final factor, set the attitude to forty five degrees with a grit of 3,000.

Next, dip the polished stone in acetone and get rid of it after 12 hours.

And you are finished!

Faceting Project four: Topaz

For this task, we are able to be doing a contemporary round, super layout:

Materials Required

- Faceting device

Procedure

First, take the difficult gem and glue it onto a brass pinnacle stick.

Next, paintings on the pavilion. For this task, we can make 16 facets the usage of a 100-grit lap in advance than advancing to a 600-grit lap, then a three,000-grit lap. For this stone, I worked on the girdle till it have become round.

Next, we're able to exchange the grit to at least one,000 after which use it to problem the stone's crown.

Finally, polish the components the use of a 50,000-grit diamond lap.

And you're finished!

Faceting Project five: Free Hand Faceting

Materials Required

- Saw

- Hammer

- Chisel

- Rough

- Marker

- Parabola

Procedure

Take your difficult and mark it to the shape you choice.

Next, take the stone and start grinding. I will now not be the use of a faceting device for this one. I will use a noticed. You only want to ensure that the hose pipe connects to an precise enough water deliver.

If sawing reaches a factor in which you need extra splitting, get a hammer and a chisel and gently hammer it down.

Next, make flat surfaces.

I used a parabola to make greater specific measurements and get the popular format.

Next, do greater grinding.

As you get towards your chosen form, change the laps as required.

After you get the desired form, update the laps with one that has a excessive grit. This lap will help you do the final polish.

And you are completed.

Faceting Project 6: Tanzanite

Materials Required

- Saw

- Tanzanite

- Drip

- Faceting machine

- Two-component epoxy

- 10x loupe

- Wax

- Super glue solvent

- Dry smooth towel

- Burnout furnace

Procedure

First, placed on your equipment.

Next, get your tanzanite hard, and slice it up the usage of a found. This completely relies upon on the scale you want.

Next, grind away the inclusions.

Next, be part of the tanzanite to a two-component epoxy. Use wax to make certain the stone stays associated with the epoxy.

Next, insert the dop stick into the faceting tool and begin shaping your tanzanite. Assess the development the use of a 10X loupe as you hold shaping the stone.

Next, after doing severa rounds of the pavilion, trade your laps and keep grinding and shaping your gemstone.

For that polished appearance, change the lap into one with a high grit, exercise some diamond powder on the lap, then preserve grinding.

Next, unhook the gem from the epoxy, shift aspects then start running at the gemstone's crown.

Next, soak the dop in a solvent —like a first-rate glue solvent— to cast off the epoxy and loose the faceted gem.

Next, take a towel and dry off the gemstone.

Finally, warmth your tanzanite the usage of a burnout furnace to approximately

1,050 stages Fahrenheit. Heating will get rid of the yellow, leaving a wealthy blue-violet colour (this is the color that tanzanite is well-known for).

And you're completed!

Faceting Project 7: Peridot

We will reduce this tough using a trillian layout lessen.

Materials Required

- Peridot hard

- Marker

- Faceting tool

- Aluminum oxide relatively-lap

Procedure

First, put on your protective gear.

Next, get your hard and determine which shape and duration you can art work on or need. If you need to reduce the tough's size, take a marker, and mark round it.

Next, restore the difficult to the dop after which begin grinding on the faceting device. The first lap I will use is a ceramic disc. I am the use of this disc because it changed into the flattest disc I had on the time. On top of the ceramic disk, add a six hundred-grit topper.

Next, as quickly as you have got were given satisfied with the results from the 600-grit, enhance to a 1,two hundred-grit.

For sharpening the stone, I used aluminum oxide extraordinarily. I decided on this because it's miles disposable and due to the aluminum oxide on one of the aspects. If you operate the equal, ensure the colourful elements face on top.

Next, facet the crown.

Finally, take the stone from the dop and dry it.

Faceting Project 8: Faceting Thai Style

Materials Required

- Saw

- Rough gemstone

- Super glue

- Touch of diamond powder

- Water

- Alcohol answer

- Soft towel

Procedure

First, placed to your shielding system.

Next, test your gemstone and decide on your preferred cut and shape.

Next, get your observed running and begin pre-forming the gemstone.

The subsequent step is to dop your stone. For this venture, I may be the use of brilliant glue.

Next, do greater pre-forming. You can determine to do the crown or the pavilion first.

Next, take a grinder that could be given unique grits and keep grinding and sprucing. However, earlier than beginning the sharpening technique, practice a touch of diamond powder.

Finally, take the stone from the dop and soak it in an alcohol answer. Then, take a clean towel and dry the stone.

And you are performed!

Step 4: Tumbling and Polishing

If you have got special kinds of rocks and would like to show them into stones and gemstones used to make crafts, rings, or decorations, do not pass for faceting; rather, pass for tumbling.

What Rocks Are Perfect For Tumbling?

If you are a lapidary novice, handiest artwork on newbie-quality rocks such as:

Aventurine

Tiger's eye

Jasper

Agate

Quartz

Moonstone

Dalmatian stone

Feldspars

Petrified wood

Hematite

Obsidian

What Rock Texture Should Rocks Ideal for Tumbling Have?

Tumbling is first-class for hard, dense, and smooth rocks!

For hardness, your rocks need to be amongst 6 and 8 on the Mohs hardness scale. On this scale, 1 is constantly regarded due to the truth the softest while 10 —diamond— is considered the toughest.

With this table in mind, the high-quality rock for tumbling have to rank among 6 and eight. If you operate rocks with a hardness of 6 and below, it technique the gem is surely smooth, and taking walks on them the usage of this method can also damage them.

On the possibility hand, the usage of too-difficult rocks will need a unique grit and quite a while in a tumbler (more on this hastily). If you need to use harder gems, use a vibratory tumbler (we also can talk extra on tumblers underneath).

You also can tumble gentle rocks, however this isn't endorsed for novices because rocks with a hardness under 6 may not take a fantastic polish. All the ones rocks will do is take shipping of a spherical and easy form, however they may lack that rich, nice, and splendid forestall end result.

The rock have to actually have a easy texture. If your rock is gritty, grainy, or sandy, DO NOT use it as hard due to the fact at the same time as those forms of rocks are broken, the ground will now not be clean to touch. To take a look at for smoothness, look for a gem without a grains signal. So, rub the rocks together and word if small rocks are being produced. If there's no grainy substance produced, the rock is best for tumbling.

It is also vital to check the hard for any fractures. If you find out any rocks which have seen cracks or fractures, put off them from the batch. If most of all of the rocks have seen fractures and also you should use them, cut up them alongside the fractures, then tumble the pieces.

Finally, the rock period subjects.

Your tumbling difficult ought to include rocks among ½ inches and 1-half of of inches in duration. Rocks larger than this may be too large for the tumblers, so they'll no longer get tumbled as required.

I moreover advocate mixing the sizes among the ½ and the 1-half of of inches. This combination will create a richer tumbling movement within the barrel because of the truth the touch surfaces will rub in the route of every specific extra (this could boom the overall performance of the tumbling).

Now that we comprehend what rocks to apply and which can be exceptional for this manner, what rock tumbling tools are we able to want? Let us list them subsequent.

Rock Tumbling Supplies

Rock tumbler grit

Grit is a substance manufactured from silicon carbide that we mounted a tumbler to make grinding much less difficult. In the faceting gadget, you can furthermore use silicon carbide, however that isn't always much like what we are able to use to tumble our rocks.

Silicon carbide is one of the high-quality for tumbling because it has a hardness of 9 at the Mohs scale. In addition to being perfectly difficult for tumbling, this substance will now not go with the flow unnecessarily throughout tumbling, ensuing in lightly tumbled rocks.

Rock sprucing grit

For sprucing, we can need rock sprucing grit. Unlike rock tumbling grit, rock sharpening grit will assist us polish our stones. For polishing, you have got have been given severa choices, along with;

- Cerium oxide

- Chrome oxide

- Aluminum oxide

- Tin oxide

Aluminum oxide is the most inexpensive, making it common. However, you may moreover buy cerium and tin oxide due to the fact they're considered all-spherical polishers. Specifically, tin oxide is perfect for softer stones, at the same time as cerium oxide is quality for obsidian and glass.

As a factor of be aware, NEVER mixture those polishes as this may decrease the results practicable if you use an man or woman polish.

Since grit is grainy, you're in all likelihood curious and questioning, "How plenty grit want to I use?"

Well, permit us to answer this subsequent:

How a whole lot grit need to you operate?

I advise the use of one tablespoon for each 4 kilos of rock for the tumbling technique and one tablespoon of sprucing grit for every pound of rock. However, if you see grit at the lowest of the tumbler after in step with week, that is a sign which you have used an excessive amount of grit.

What grit sizes for the tumbling and sprucing do you want?

Grit is available in severa tiers this is 60-90, a hundred fifty-220, and 500. For faster grinding, particularly whilst walking with tough rocks, it's miles higher to apply forty five-70 grit.

Please phrase that there are four ranges of grit:

- Stage 1 requires forty five-70 frit or 60-ninety grit — that is extraordinary for tough rocks

- Stage 2 would require 100 fifty-220 grit — that is amazing for smoothening all of the hard edges. In addition, this grit will assist take away huge scratches from the rocks.

- Stage three could require 500 grit – this grit will put together your rocks for the final polish. For some rocks, this grit will offer the rocks a polished appearance.

- Finally, level four may require polish grit.

Once you finish working with grit, please do no longer be involved approximately in which to dispose it due to the truth it's miles non-toxic. You can dispose it within the woods or a driveway. Be eager not to sell off it on grass as it will suffocate the grass —that means the grass will not get any or sufficient water and mild.

Rock tumblers

This may be our critical tool. As you could inform from the picture, a rock tumbler is a gadget. We will located our rocks in it with a combination of grit and water; then, after last it up, it's miles going to reveal spherical and spherical until the stone becomes as gentle as we need them to be.

There exists 2 forms of rock tumblers:

Rotary tumblers

Vibratory tumblers

Rotary tumblers are the most not unusual and are great for beginners. They are ideal for knocking out the rocks' form at the equal time as smoothening tough rocks. Fundamentally, rotary tumblers are great for converting a rock's shape, giving your rocks a extra-rounded appearance.

On the alternative hand, vibratory tumblers aren't so common because of the reality they are higher for sharpening already-common rocks. Therefore, this sort of tumbler will no longer form your rocks, but a rotary tumbler will.

What is an appropriate rock tumbler period for tumbling?

Most beginners begin operating closer to tumbling the usage of a 3-pound tumbler. If that is what you can purchase, kindly be conscious that it'll keep 2 kilos of rock and 1 pound of grit and water. If you have got were given precise styles of rock, purchase a double-barrel rotary tumbler.

Plastic Pellets

As mentioned earlier in bankruptcy three, those pellets will fill the gap within the tumbler whilst you positioned the rocks in and assist benefit a better polish at the stop of the technique. In addition, pellets add extra cushioning, thereby minimizing the rock's impact in opposition to the tumbler.

With our device and rocks equipped, it's time to tumble!

Before we get to high-quality tumbling responsibilities, here's a summarized model of what the tumbling procedure entails:

Rock Tumbling Stage 1: Shaping the Rough

- We will first fill our tumbler's barrel with rocks of diverse sizes up to 2-thirds of its fill. If you do now not have sufficient rocks to fill it to that degree, upload some plastic pellets rapid after together with the rocks.

- The subsequent step might be to add the grit and water —in this series— then near the barrel tightly.

- Next, we will study the barrel's weight, then start the gadget. This is because of the fact the tumbler has its maximum weight, making it critical to verify that we do no longer surpass this restriction.

- After each week of non-prevent tumbling, we will take a look at the stones. If their shape is thrilling, we can take away the rocks after which rinse them with clean water. Should the stones no longer have the shape we desire after the number one week, we are capable of put them again inside the tumbler and tumble them until we get the famous shape.

- After taking the stones out of the barrel, we can smooth the tumbler's barrel with water and cleansing soap. After it dries, we can go to the subsequent diploma.

Rock Tumbling Stage 2: Tumbling the medium/exceptional grit

- We will re-do the preliminary stage 1's techniques and ensure we add pellets if needed. Our reason in this diploma is to eliminate all scratches, pits, and cracks, consequently growing a silly glow after the rocks dry up.

- We will take a look at on the rocks' kingdom each day. After achieving the favored nation, we can go to the subsequent stage: pre-sprucing the stones.

Rock Tumbling Stage 3: Pre-Polishing the Rocks

In this stage, we're capable of do similar to stages 1 and a couple of.

We will allow the rocks tumble for about one week, but this time can also additionally furthermore change depending at the u . S . A . Of the rocks. After disposing of the rocks from the tumbler, we can smooth them and the barrel, then go to the final diploma.

Rock Tumbling Stage 4: Polishing the Rocks

This diploma entails the usage of the sprucing grit and letting the rocks tumble for in keeping with week, and at the same time as it comes time to rinse the rocks, our rocks have to have a rich, vibrant shine! However, if the rocks will not have the brightness we preference, a few thing mainly common even as tumbling jaspers and agates, we will go to the very last level.

Rock Tumbling Stage 5: Burnishing the Polished Rocks

This diploma would require us to apply powdered laundry detergent or cleansing cleaning soap in region of polishing grit (we are able to use about tablespoons for every pound of rock). Tumbler masters say doing this may upload greater shine to the rocks, brighten them similarly, and cast off any residue from them.

Before asserting that our rocks want this level, we are able to do a smooth test. To try this test, we are able to do the subsequent;

- Take one of the rocks and rub it with a gentle towel for approximately 20 seconds.

- If the aspect we rub shines brighter than the other factors of the rock, it way the rock wishes a burnishing diploma.

We will burnish the stones for twenty-4 hours, rinse them, and be executed with the way.

The mystery to this entire approach is PATIENCE!

Now that we understand what to expect, we're capable of begin doing specific initiatives to position the precept to paintings;

Rock Tumbling Project 1: Tumbling Without a Tumbling Machine

Materials Required

- Tumbler

- Rocks

- Grit

- Pellets

- Food scale

- Water

- Ivory cleaning cleaning cleaning soap

- Knife

- Dish cleaning soap

Procedure

- First, acquire your rocks and located them on your barrel.

Next, upload your plastic pellets. Remember that everything within the barrel have to skip all way to 2-thirds entire.

Next, add water till you get to the top of the rocks.

Next, add your grit. Use a meals scale to take measurements and apprehend how plenty grit you want. Remember, every tumbler has its weight written on it; use that to recognize how a outstanding deal grit you want.

Next, cover the tumbler with a lid and permit it rest for steady with week. After every week, rinse it off and decide the rocks.

You will observe that the tumbler seems much like the first-class underneath. When I opened my tumbler, and after draining the liquid aggregate and taking the stones off, I said that I had some stones stuck at the lowest.

This occurred due to the reality I installed too much grit. So, to treatment the scenario, I will try to get it off with a toothbrush.

With the relaxation of the rocks easy, rinse the stones and affirm them. From mine, I can also want to pinpoint some rocks that have been prepared to transport directly to the following degree. To look at which rocks are geared up to move to the following degree, look for ones that look greater rounded.

Below is one of the rocks that are not organized to transport to the following degree:

So, for the rocks that have now not in truth surpassed to the subsequent degree, we are capable of grit them the identical way we did for degree 1. The distinction is that we're able to no longer tumble them for the overall seven days because of the truth we do not need to lose too much material.

For this 2d diploma-1-repeat, lessen the wide kind of grit and pellet amount, and examine the rocks after five days. For this try, no stones remained stuck below the tumbler. Below is our quit result.

If you are satisfied with the consequences, go to the subsequent diploma. Before going to the next diploma, rinse the stones with ivory cleaning soap. Additionally, once you upload the cleaning soap and the water to the rocks, permit them to tumble for a day.

After an afternoon, rinse it off and go to step 2. Follow the same steps we used within the first stage but keenly close to the quantity of grit you put in. I might not like you to make a large range as I did in level 1.

Repeat the identical approach for the following tiers. We can start our sharpening at degree four; I used notable aluminum oxide. Close the tumbler and allow it relaxation for about 3 weeks.

Assess them, then take each of them and scrub. This will take the polish off.

If the rocks are as you need them to be, go to the following step. For the following step, placed the rocks in the tumbler, add water and some dish cleaning cleansing soap, and depart it for an afternoon.

Next, rinse them off and brush them off. I propose the use of a softer brush, which includes a toothbrush this time.

Finally, dry them off, and that's it for this assignment!

Rock Tumbling Project 2: Tumbling with a Rock Tumbler

For this challenge, we are able to use a 15-pound tumbler.

Materials Required

- Tumbler

- Grit tumbler

- Grit polisher

- Rough rocks

- Sieve

Chapter 6: Gems And Stones Appraisal

As a lapidarist entering into gem stones and precious stones promoting, you want to anticipate and appearance an extended way and big. That method promoting to close by pawn stores, cash-for-gold shops, consignment stores, vintage dealers, diamond exchanges, diamond consumers, gemstone dealers, and other jewelers, together with all on line sellers.

When you get a patron, what do you need to understand about valuable stone and gem grading?

Understanding Precious Stone and Gem Grading

The key issue to do not forget is that there is NO preferred incredible grading, as affirmed with the useful resource of the Gemological Institute of America.[24]

Precious Stones and Gems Selling Tips

That referred to, proper right here are a few key topics to phrase and keep in thoughts to make sure which you sell your stones on the great fee viable:

Understand the Gem and Stone Color Interpretation

We classify gemstones into colorings, tones, and saturations.

- Hue sun shades are pink, violet, blue, green, yellow, orange, and pink.

- Tones and saturations are brown, white, and black. Why the ones hues? Well, tone refers to how moderate or darkish a stone is. Saturation refers back to the depth of the gem's hue —whether or not or not the colour is every slight or sturdy.

Leverage the electricity of your reduce

The projects we've got were given discussed thus far have awesome artistry. The first-rate manner to set a charge in your gem is to use the art work you positioned into it. If you've got labored to create cuts that reflect the most quantity of moderate, rest confident that those cuts receives you more money.

Also, keep in mind that in case you contain your reduce with duration, i.E., making larger, more conspicuous stones and gems that reflect the maximum amount of mild, you will be in a better feature to price greater.

Always purchase unusual and various treasured stones and gems

Expect to rate more in case you paintings on traditional gemstones which incorporates Sapphires, Emeralds, Diamonds, and Rubies due to the fact they are pretty unusual. Moreover, despite the fact that those stones are pricier, get the most high-priced and artwork on those.

For instance, rubies are a ways rarer than sapphires, and strolling with them manner you could earn extra from your projects. If you may hunt down a Burma ruby, then the better due to the reality it's miles the rarest of the gemstones appeared!

Ensure your valuable stones and gem stones are as smooth as feasible

While deciding on your hard, recall that your charge will skyrocket if your work produces a smooth precious stone, even when running on coloured or colored stones and gem stones.

Therefore, undertaking to deliver artwork with out a visible inclusions, in spite of the reality that stones with inclusions also can be steeply-priced.

Clarity is crucial specifically due to the fact famous gem and stone grading uses the categorization beneath:

- Grade AA-AAA: This grade encompasses stones with the following attributes:

- It is flawlessly faceted

- It is taken into consideration perfect to the bare eye

- The coloration isn't always extra applicable

- It is mainly apparent

- This grade is commonly reserved for precious gems together with sapphires, emeralds, rubies, garnets, and amethyst.

- A-B Grade: This grade functions stones and gem stones with the subsequent function:

- The stones on this elegance are nicely reduce, have mild coloration versions, are averagely apparent, and feature inclusions.

- C-D Grade: The gem stones and stones in this grade have the subsequent attributes;

- The stones and gemstones under this grade have more inclusions, are lowly obvious, are available one-of-a-type styles and cuts, and are available in extra huge colour versions.

Think about carat and recognition

Earlier, we stated that we weigh treasured stones and gems in carats.

Well:

That technique the bigger the carat, the higher the price. Why? Well, it's far hard and greater luxurious to discover a massive-sized diamond hard. In addition, popularity may have an impact on the manner you sell your stones and gemstones. You see, certain weights inclusive of one and a pair of.5 carats, are famous due to the reality the marketplace, along facet the diamond market, is incredibly unstable as regards to deliver and speak to for.

Chapter 7: Lapidary Butterfly

]

This challenge started out at some point of a vacation in Idar-Oberstein. This is a niche in Germany seemed for its gems. There are furthermore numerous little plant life and atteliers which paintings with gemstones.

During a go to to this sort of flora, in which hardware for drug shops is created, there was a posibility to look for gemstones. As a rely style of fact there was a heap of waste, with all shape of gemstones.

The perception modified into to make a mozaic, as a gift. With as stop end result this sizeable butterfly mozaic (forty four x 30 inches, 110 x 75 cm).

Various gadgets are required for the handling of gemstones. Progressively, a discovered, a seat processor and a cleaning machine. These machines are intended for coping with gem stones, regrettably they have got a associated decal rate. That is the purpose I've all commenced to search for picks.

In this e book I depict the way to make a mosaic with gemstones. Predominantly with the use of pressure apparatuses, supplemented for effective home made devices.

Stage 1: Junk to Prize

As referenced the gem stones for this mosaic have been observed at some point of a vacation in Idar-Oberstein. These lay on a primary heap, collectively with large agate diamonds. These stones have been now not reasonable for brought coping with. Yet, what's squander for this plant, is a lovable and modest item to make some thing particular.

It earlier than long grew to become out to make certain that few types of waste stones had been tossed on this heap. Furthermore, not without a doubt huge quantities of agate. Yet moreover extra modest portions of amethyst, quartz and super gemstones.

We came to the plan to make a mosaic. What's extra, in mild of this, we started out out gathering colorfull stage bits of jewels. Furthermore, within the path of the finish of the midday we have been 50 euro extra unlucky, but a field loaded with diamonds extra extravagant. Also, inside the wake of arranging the stones, we had the accompanying styles of gemstones:

Red Agate (6.Five - 7)

Green Agate (6.Five - 7)

Dark Agate (6.Five - 7)

Quarts (7)

Rose Quarts (7)

Aventurine (inexperienced) (7)

Lapis Lazuli (blue, five - 6)

Sodalite (blue, five.Five - 6)

Citrine (yellow, 7)

Citrine (dim, 7)

Amethyst (red, 7)

Amazonite (astounding green, 6 - 6.Five)

Red Jasper (6,5 - 7)

Tiger's Eye (6,five-7)

Caution:

In this ebook I use power gadgets, which aren't meant for running with gemstones. Continuously utilize right protection hardware. This beginnings with a outstanding residue cowl, goggles and ear safety.

Particularly my tool for cleaning the diamonds requires alert. It joins energy, cleaning specialist, and water to smooth the gem stones. Continuously do away with the attachment from the attachment preceding to supplanting the gems. Furthermore, employ a ground trouble interrupter for the wiring on your hardware.

Stage 2: Required Materials

Notwithstanding the gem stones, the accompanying materials are required:

Wood (4 x 3 ft, 122 x ninety centimeter) . I've applied a relaxation of 18mm pressed timber.

Silicon Carbide grating powder K-80

Silicon Carbide grating powder K-220

Silicon Carbide grating powder K-4 hundred

Silicon Carbide grating powder K-800

Alumina Powder

Polypropylene Plastic Pellets

Straightforward Paste (three hundred ml tube)

Grout

Felt (4mm, network hobbystore)

Carbon Paper (a hundred and twenty x 80 cm)

Geode (for the sensors).

The cleansing substances (silicon carbide) has a moh's clearly properly worth of nine to nine.Five. Cleaning alumina powder has a moh's properly really worth of nine. For this reason we can make use of those substances to clean gems.

Stage 3: Butterfly Example

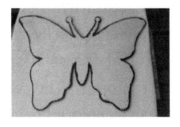

Subsequent to gathering and arranging of the gems the time had come to pick out what to make. The number one perception modified into to layout a mirror. At final, we've picked this butterfly. This picture may no longer have this form of large huge sort of subtleties, however it has every one of the features of a butterfly.

Convert this image to a Gymnastic performer/PDF-file. Furthermore, print out the plan as an massive banner (3x3 or 4x4 pages).

Draw the past the patern on a bit of compressed timber. Utilize a jigsaw to get rid of the butterfly. Furthermore, paint the complete butterfly with white basis. This works at the solar sunglasses of the honest stones. The outside is painted with earthy colored paint.

Draw inside the butterfly utilising carbon paper.

Fill the example with gemstones to determine the proper variety layout. This gives a belief of the predicted kind of stones for every tone.

Stage four: Rock Tumbler

For the tumbling of the stones I've offered a Lortone tumbler drum. Not the entire tumbler, however alternatively clearly the vital drum (spherical forty five euro). I make use of an antique cordless drill for pivoting the drum. Alongside a five volt electricity deliver from an vintage outer hard strength. Because of the low burden, and decrease voltage, the engine isn't always strolling excessively warmth.

A metallic pole (eight mm) in the bore fills in as a stress shaft. Two extra wheels guarantee that the drum can flip. The cordless drill is positioned on a rack, the use of a cinch. With a 2d clasp at the strength transfer.

Notwithstanding the drum, I genuinely have worried numerous types of cleaning powder and plastic pellets in this step:

Silicon Carbide grating powder K-80

Silicon Carbide grating powder K-220

Silicon Carbide grating powder K-four hundred

Silicon Carbide grating powder K-800

Alumina Powder

Polypropylene Plastic Pellets

Fill the drum approximately 1/2 of complete with gems. Add 2 tablespoons of tough powder. Cover the stones with water. Also, near the drum appropriately. Allow the drum to pivot for multiple hours (four-eight hours).

It isn't the reason to get absolutely roundabout stones. The stones should be ideal. Also, the real variety should be good sized, with a few cleansing impact.

After this number one round, easy the gem stones in a field of water (no longer inside the sink). Furthermore, rehash this cycle, on every occasion with a better difficult powder (K220, K400 and K800). The last step is makes use of a mix of aluminum oxide and poly props. This step gives the closing shine.

Remember to clean the drum between every step. You want no coarser grating powder within the drum preceding to persevering with to the following degree. So it's far smarter to start with all the unsightly art work. Begin tumbling with the coarse powder. This saves time to clean the drum. Furthermore, it likewise saves a great deal of water, that you can not toss straightforwardly into the channel.

Stage five: Section and Trim Saw

There are two types of noticed while operating with pearls:

Chunk saws are implemented to make get segment slices through gems.

Trim saws are executed for dealing with slim sections.

We predominantly gathered little level gemstones. Most stones we determined have been at that trouble reduce with an expert found. So I did not need to discovered a huge range. In any case, for the couple of stones I had to found, I implemented a top notch tile observed. This is supplied with a jewel sharp element with water cooling. It is appreciably loads much less costly than an brilliant noticed for gem stones.

A tile noticed is not the maximum first-class technique for gem stones. It is achievable on the off risk that you waft the gemstones gradually. The drawback is that the ones gems, which might be dealt with with a tile determined, require more publish managing. Since the lessen is plenty much less lovely.

To eliminate little bits of (dainty) gemstone you could more without a problem utilize a seat processor.

Stage 6: Vibrating Lap

A vibrating lap is implemented for cleansing degree gem stones. Due to the excessive fee of a diploma dish, I commenced via using making my non-public shape.

The crucial version have turn out to be an antique aluminum teflon baking dish installed on an electrical sander. This gave a vibrating field. Sadly, it did no longer smooth the stones pretty properly. Likewise a sander isn't work to transport the heaviness of a subject. I have become disturbing about the opportunity that that it'd destroy down all at once.

One more technique for cleansing gems is floor crushing on a piece of glass. Simply take a bit of glass, cleansing expert and a few water. Presently circulate the gemstone in a roundabout manner. Thus, the stone can be wiped smooth. To try this thru hand is an extended interplay.

At a fantastic aspect, I began the usage of a sander to move the stones. This elevated the cycle, however it is no longer in reality some component unique to perform for pretty a while.

At ultimate I made a timber subject (2d image). Fairly huge than the sander (1/four inch). In this I area a piece of felt (four mm thick) with a similar period due to the truth the case. I positioned stage bits of gem stones (with a similar thickness and moh's really worth) on top of this residue of felt. Next I introduced water and a couple of teaspoons of easy. The final layer is a next piece (moist) felt with the dimensions of the sander.

The sander can go along with the waft unreservedly in the case. Furthermore, turning at the system will smooth the stones. This functioned admirably. Ensure the felt should not dry out. The whole should live moist. Also, test the manner each hour.

Working with a vibrating lap includes similar strides as running with a stone tumbler. Utilize frequently better cleaning fabric after every step. You ought to genuinely smooth the container after every step, to save you polution of the following diploma. Furthermore, don't forget to supplant the felt.

The combination of power (improvement), and water (cleaning) requires a few discipline. Eliminate the wonderful out of the attachment previous to minding the gems. What's more, Spot this in an enormous plastic holder.

If it is now not too much trouble, be conscious, this interaction takes a top notch deal of time.

Stage 7: Seat Processor

Along with the power sander, this device has been applied for more regularly than now not. This grindstone turned into sold at a community device hold. These system are not supposed to be accomplished with water. In any case, the whole thing appears incredible for the use of this machine with little water. Simply make sure that the principle (electrical) additives do now not get moist.

I commenced this task with the protected crushing stones. This worked for typically estimating the stones. In any case, I observed that the grindstone unexpectedly breaks down even as carried out with gems.

After ugly changing of the gem stones, it showed that the gemstones are more earnestly than the crushing wheel.

Furthermore, it became out to be often tough to get a directly reduce. Therefore I modified to a jewel crushing stone (spherical 40 euros, search for "one hundred and fifty mm jewel crushing wheel Ukraine" on EBay).

The precious stone grindstone have end up almost essentially as steeply-priced due to the fact the seat processor itself. Be that as it may, it surely works glaringly superior to the furnished grindstones. Furthermore, it indicates no apparent placed on, even within the wake of coping with all stones for this butterfly.

In the wake of measuring the stones, they had been wiped clean for a totally last time body. I supplanted all felt, and concerned alumina as a cleansing expert.

Stage 8: Butterfly Mosaic

In the wake of finishing all gem stones, the time has come to place them at the wood casing. First take a few snap shots, for the unique spots of every stone. Clean all stones with cleanser and water and allow them to dry.

I've applied the accompanying amount of gem stones:

Red Agate (29)

Green Agate (37)

Dark Agate (6)

Amazonite (37)

Amethyst (forty eight)

Aventurine (34)

Citrine (12)

Dull Citrine (40 four)

Lapis Lazuli (40)

Quarts (8)

Red Jaspis (10)

Rhodonite (2)

Rose Quarts (34)

Sodalite (25)

Tiger's Eye (6)

A sum of 374 gemstones.

Stage nine: Connect the Gemstones

In the wake of cleansing and placing the stones is a perfect possibility to stick them.

The wooden ground is painted white, however at the equal no longer sanded. This offers greater draw near for the paste. Utilize honest cement and make certain the stones are uniformly separated.

There is a few distinction in stage a number of the gems. Since the awesome stone sections aren't same in thickness. This may be addressed via along with extra paste. Be that as it could, it isn't the purpose to get a totally degree ground. I make upgraded this difference, and stuck the rose quarts with the unpleasant aspect on the the the front.

Stage 10: Mosaic Grout

While operating with grout I implemented extensively more water than confirmed at the package deal. Because of the unpredictable design of particular gem stones, I would possibly have as an opportunity no longer protected the whole butterfly with grout. It might take a superb deal of efforts to eliminate all exorbitant grout thereafter.

I've placed the concrete straightforwardly some of the stones, the use of a needle. This must be finished assuming the grout is sort of fluid. Continuously cast off the overabundance grout with water and a superb cloth.

We furthermore made a version using dark grout. In this number one example the grout leaked below the transparant gems. This can be addressed via using greater paste underneath the ones stones. At lengthy last we've choosen white grout. It made the tones greater energetic.

Chapter 8: Prologue To Lapidary Adornments Making

This is for any individual who wishes to get into gem stones making, but does not have the foggiest concept in which to start. When you wrap up perusing this e-book, you will be aware:

a. Which gem stones making kind is first-class for you

what's extra,

b. Instructions to begin

The schooling are:

1. Wire wrapping

2. Wire winding round

3. Freestyle wrapping

four. Wire craftsmanship

5. Silversmithing

6. Beading

Stage 1: WIRE WRAPPING

Wire wrapping is my undisputed top choice form of adornments making.

We can start simplifying, but high-quality topics, with a tiny degree of gadgets. Additionally, we are capable of beautify as short as we experience.

Wire professionals art work with diverse metals like copper, silver, gold, and metallic.

There are three crucial kinds of cord gemstones: WIRE WRAPPING, WIRE winding around and Freestyle WRAPPING. There is also a few different category known as WIRE Craftsmanship.

What's going on right right right here?

Wire wrapping is taking a cabbed rock, a dab, or some aspect outstanding, and wrapping it with kinds of wire to make it right right into a pendant or a chunk on your gem stones.

Fundamental wire wrap:

Begin with gem professionals pincers, numerous assessments/states of wires, and a taxi. A taxi is a stone that has been molded on a gadget called a stone processor.

Then take rectangular wires and a few half of of spherical wires and make it right into a %.

From that component in advance, fold the organization over the taxi and interface it at the pinnacle.

The very last step is to do the diletantish contacts, and it is completed.

My essential aspect approximately this is we can take any critical plan and in a while change it right into a endless diploma of severa plans.

To get the whole thing rolling:

When we recognize the basics, then, at that factor, we can find greater motivation on the internet and use it to help us with acquiring new competencies.

Neighborhood rock and mineral stores commonly have wire artwork examples as nicely.

Stage 2: WIRE Winding around

Wire winding round is a laugh however thoughts boggling and tedious. It's not precisely a incredible one for fledglings because it takes a hint of schooling to consummate your piece. Yet, the very last product may be ideal.

Wire winding spherical is like critical cord wrapping, but it makes use of substantially more cord. You might also need to absolutely use north of one hundred toes of cord handiest for one pendant. Weavers typically absolutely copper because of the fact that it is lots less high priced than one-of-a-type metals.

This photo is one in every of my absolute first twine weave duties as a beginner.

What is it:

Wire winding around is type of equivalent to wire wrapping, aside from you wrap severa examples with the cord and layer the instance wires proper proper right into a entire swinging.

An Essential weave:

We'll require, goldsmiths forceps, wires of numerous checks and shapes, and a taxi or dot.

First we start with the aid of winding round an instance with the cord. Next fold it over the taxi. Then, at that thing, add greater designed cord till you get a larger pendant.

To get the whole lot rolling:

Figuring out a way to do cord wrapping first earlier than we attempt to wire weave may be a awesome initial step.

Stage 3: FREE Structure WIRE WRAP

What is it:

Free form is the component at which we do no longer have a completely unique affiliation before we start. It's the detail at which we allow the materials to guide us as we technique making our piece, with materials like wires, globules, rocks, and moreover gems.

Fundamental freestyle:

We'll start with multiple pincers, a few twine, and a gem or big dot.

Begin by using way of the use of stringing the wires via the hole within the globule or folding it over the treasured stone. Next make a circle at the pinnacle. Then, at that factor, take the possibility wires and truely have an wonderful time with it.

To start:

Most distinctiveness shops supply foxy wire and huge dab pendants.

Stage 4: WIRE Workmanship

Wire workmanship is certainly one of my pinnacle alternatives. It's typically finished via proficient people. It takes a bit of schooling to encourage it to look outstanding, yet it is in reality clearly well worth the strive inside the event that you have the patience to widely recognized a couple of faulty portions towards the begin of the developing revel in. At last we're going to start to see the portions will more regularly than not get very particular after a while the greater we're grinding away. It can revel in overpowering or confounded sometimes at the same time as looking to get the wires to stay installation or glide the way in which you need them to.

What is it?

Wire workmanship is generally portrayed as even as the cord is more the factor of convergence and not the diamond or dot. Various measures of cord are normally used to make one piece.

Essential twine craftsmanship

Before we begin, we are going to want to attract out our plan. Next we're able to require a willpower of wires and gadgets.

I enthusiastically endorse avoid make wires because it WILL break. Make sure to encompass any dots or faced stones that we need to consolidate. Likewise make sure to deal with a diploma smooth floor.

This one is more development, so I advise attempting those above first in the event which you're a fledgling.

Stage 5: Valuable METAL SMITHING

Valuable metalsmiths art work with metals like silver, gold, copper, metallic, weld, and so on. They furthermore use gadgets like diamond setters hammer, gem dealers noticed, and lighting. Their gemstones will quite regularly look like some aspect you will discover in an adornments shop. Valuable metalsmithing is a pleasing side hobby, however it takes express devices and a few experience, however it has a tendency to very remunerate!

WHAT IS IT

Valuable metalsmithing is running with crude metals and reworking them into bits of gem stones through the most common way of slicing, warming, welding, and cleansing.

Essential PENDANT

To begin we're going to require some essential devices and materials like a taxi, crude metals, and some weld. We'll likewise require a few contraptions like pincers, gem supplier noticed, light, and severa mallets.

First hassle we are going to believe that need to do is plan it for the cause that silversmithing calls for a few funding, exertion, and cash. So we need to make sure we've got got an affiliation concept out earlier than we get the whole lot rolling.

Then, have a have a look at your taxi on a bit of diploma metallic and in a while lessen it out with a gem expert observed. From that component beforehand, we're going to take some level cord and bind it with a slight to the rims of the decrease lower back piece that we presently reduce.

This finishes the slant (Otherwise known as our essential piece). After this, we will add any embellishing portions we want to vicinity on it. Remember to function a circle or some factor to sign up for it to the jewelry.

Presently it might be a absolutely perfect possibility to feature the taxi. Lay it in the piece and in a while overwhelm the rims of the volume cord down across the taxi. The final step is to clean it thinking about the truth that it'll be oxidized and scratched up from chipping away at it.

After this is completed the pendant is carried out!

TO get the entirety rolling

Most stone and mineral stores will deliver natural materials want for this venture.

Stage 6: BEADING

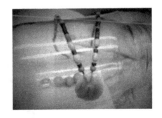

Beading is an extraordinary form of gems making. It's very a laugh and easy to get into. Dot employees paintings with dabs which may be fabricated from glass, steel, some plastics, or potentially everyday stone.

Some globule employee's make neckbands absolutely with dabs, concerning the dots as a extraordinary thing of convergence or pendant. Others globule neckbands round a pendant like a cord wrapped or silver smithed piece.

There are many dabs handy, at the facet of ones which is probably referred to as seed globules. Seed globules are minuscule similar to the duration of a natural product fly. A few craftsmen string seed dots together into really issue by using aspect and incredible portions. Different dots, as immoderate superb glass globules, are very lovely components of add to a neckband.

Personally, I need to make a pendant [usually a wire wrapped pendant] and afterward make a themed earrings with themed dabs to go together with it.

WHAT IS IT

Hanging dabs and outstanding materials into a bit of gem stones.

Fundamental Jewelry

Before you begin, you could require devices like a beading needle, forceps, and substances like dabs (bunches of them) beading string, an give up connector, and a pendant (or no longer).

To start, we will take our pendant and I coordinate it with dots that go along with the problem and range. Then take maintain of every one of the ones that appearance proper collectively. Then taking beading string or cowhide lash. I strive out numerous mixes and examples of dots to discern out which one appears proper. When we've got our example executed, we are able to rehash the example as a ways as viable across the neckband, transforming it as soon as whilst the pendant.

Printed in the USA
CPSIA information can be obtained
at www.ICGtesting.com
LVHW010009271223
767510LV00046B/1644

9 781778 247682